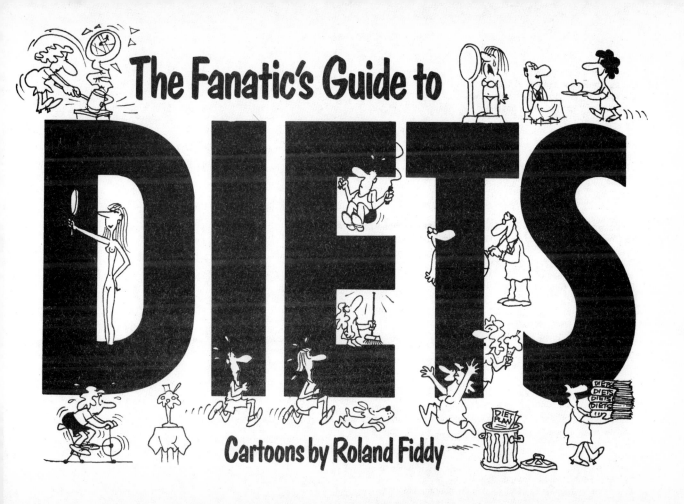

The Fanatic's Guide to DIETS

Cartoons by Roland Fiddy

Other books by Roland Fiddy,
also published by Exley Publications:
The Crazy World of the Handyman
The Crazy World of Love

In the same series:
The Fanatic's Guide to Golf
The Fanatic's Guide to Cats
The Fanatic's Guide to Sex

Published in Great Britain in 1990 by **Exley Publications Ltd,**
16 Chalk Hill, Watford, Herts WD1 4BN, United Kingdom.

Copyright © Roland Fiddy, 1990

British Library Cataloguing in Publication Data
Fiddy, Roland
  Fanatic's guide to diets.
  1. English humorous cartoons
  I. Title
  741.5942

ISBN 1-85015-238-1

Typeset by Brush Off Studios, St Albans, Herts AL3 4PH.
Printed and bound in Great Britain by
The Guernsey Press Co. Ltd, Guernsey, Channel Islands.

Roland Fiddy

Born in Plymouth, Devon in 1941. Studied at the West of England College of Art Bristol. Works as a free lance cartoonist and illustrator. His cartoons have been published in Britain, the United States and many other countries. Has taken part in International Cartoon Festivals since 1984, and has won the following awards:

1984 First Prize, Beringen, Belgium
1984 Special Prize, Tokyo, Japan
1984 Public Prize, Amsterdam, Holland.
1985 First Prize, Amsterdam, Holland.
1985 Second Prize, Knokke Heist, Belgium.
1986 First Prize, Beringen, Belgium.
1986 First Prize Amsterdam, Holland.
1986 First Prize Sofia, Bulgaria
1987 Second Prize Skopje, Yugoslavia.
1987 Casino Prize, Knokke Heist, Belgium
1987 UNESCO Prize Gabrovo Bulgaria
1987 First Prize Piracicaba, Brazil
1988 Golden Date Bordighera Italy
1988 Second Prize London England
1989 E.E.C. Prize Kruishoutem Belgium

Fiddy

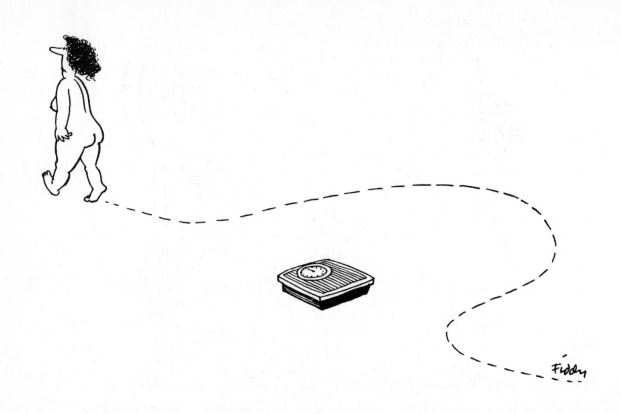

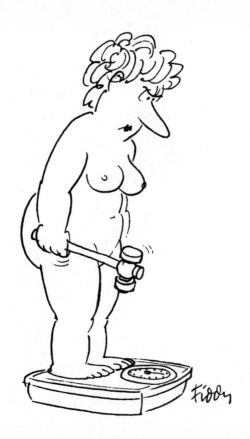

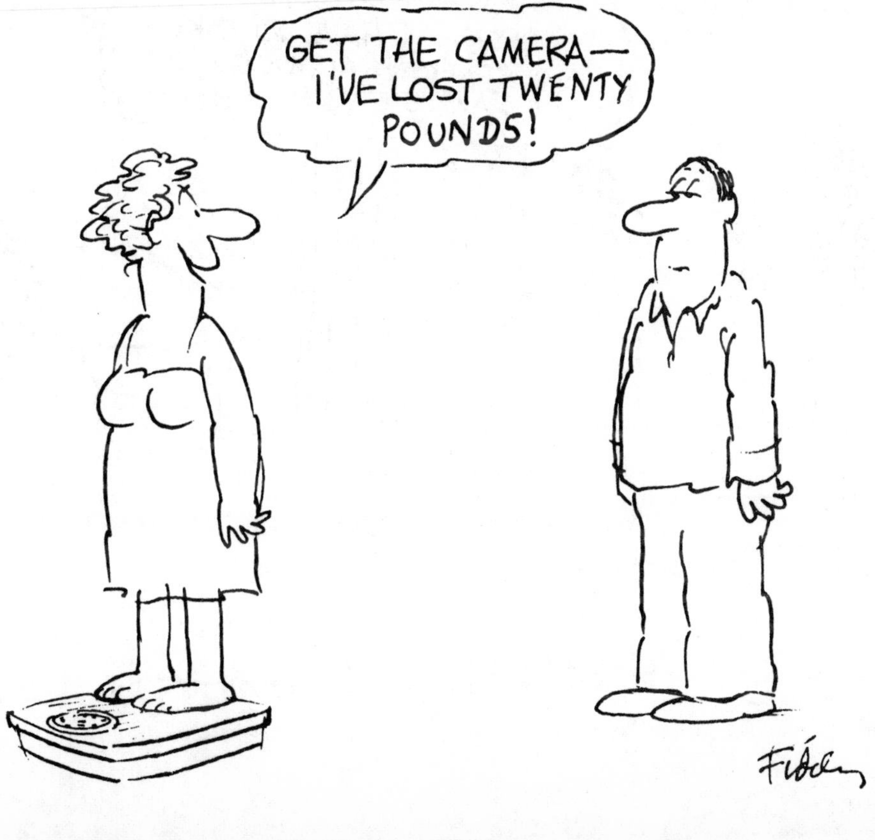
GET THE CAMERA— I'VE LOST TWENTY POUNDS!

UNFORTUNATELY THERE'S A FAT PERSON INSIDE ME STRUGGLING TO GET OUT!

GEORGE USED TO BE A **FAT** SLOB UNTIL I PUT HIM ON A DIET!

Fiddy

AIDS TO DIETING.
Willpower

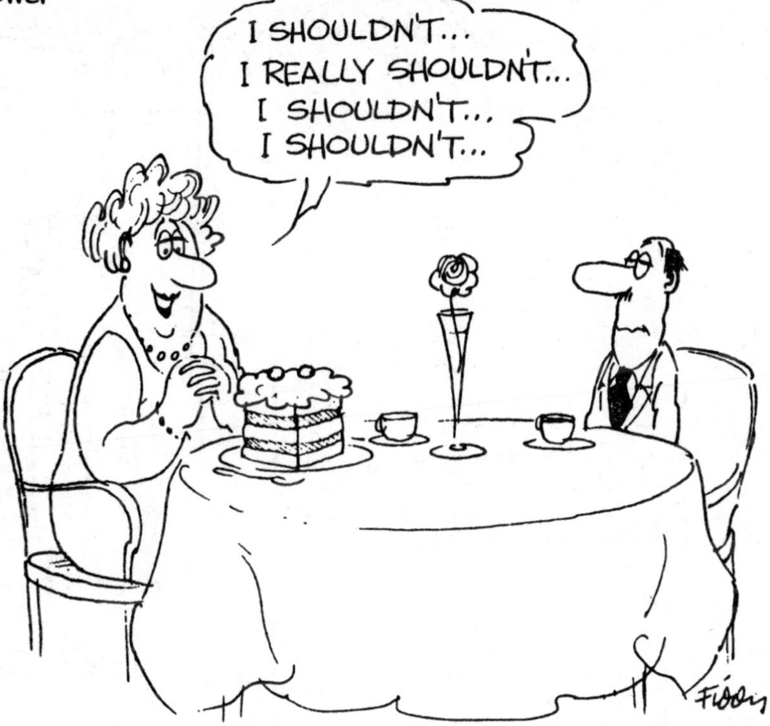

AIDS TO DIETING

Hypnotherapy. Using hypnosis, the therapist repeats over and over "You are too fat, you are too fat." Of course, some subjects are resistant to hypnosis. This can be dangerous, (for the hypnotherapist, that is.)

1.

2.

AIDS TO DIETING   The importance of exercise

ALL RIGHT, IT'S A DEAL — YOU STOP CALLING ME TUB AND I'LL STOP CALLING YOU FATSO!
Fiddy

EXCLUSIVE HEALTH FARM.

In the Same Series:

The Fanatic's Guide to Cats

(£2.99 paperback). A must for cat lovers everywhere who cannot fail to find fun and laughter in the frolics of our feline friends.

The Fanatic's Guide to Golf

(£2.99 paperback) is one gift that the golfer will love. The **Fanatic's Guides** are perfect presents everyone with a hobby that has got out of hand . . .

The Fanatic's Guide to Sex

(£2.99 paperback). For lovers everywhere — it will have them falling on their backs in no time — with laughter!

The Crazy World series (£3.99 hardback).
There are now 18 different titles in this best-selling cartoon series — one of them must be right for a friend of yours . . .

The Crazy World of Birdwatching (Peter Rigby)
The Crazy World of Cats (Bill Stott)
The Crazy World of Cricket (Bill Stott)
The Crazy World of Gardening (Bill Stott)
The Crazy World of Golf (Mike Scott)
The Crazy World of the Handyman (Roland Fiddy)
The Crazy World of Hospitals (Bill Stott)
The Crazy World of Jogging (David Pye)
The Crazy World of Love (Roland Fiddy)
The Crazy World of Marriage (Bill Stott)
The Crazy World of Music (Bill Stott)
The Crazy World of the Office (Bill Stott)
The Crazy World of Photography (Bill Stott)
The Crazy World of Rugby (Bill Stott)
The Crazy World of Sailing (Peter Rigby)
The Crazy World of Sex (David Pye)
The Crazy World of Skiing (Craig Peterson & Jerry Emerson)
The Crazy World of Tennis (Peter Rigby)

Great Britain: these books make super presents. Order them from you local bookseller or from Exley Publications Ltd.